ALLURING ANDROIDS, ROBOT WOMEN, AND ELECTRONIC EVES

JULIE WOSK

FORT SCHUYLER PRESS

NEW YORK

ISBN: 0-9670328-5-1

Fort Schuyler Press
State University of New York
Maritime College
Department of Humanities
6 Pennyfield Avenue
Throggs Neck, New York 10465
www.sunymaritime.edu

PREFACE

Several years ago, I sat in a darkened room in a small art museum in Neuchâtel, Switzerland while a technician gave me a demonstration of one of the museum's prized possessions: an elegantly-dressed lady automaton built in the eighteenth century by the master Swiss clockmakers Pierre and Henri-Louis Jaquet-Droz (Fig. 5). As her fingers deftly played an organ in the shape of a harpsichord, her eyes moved quickly from side-to-side—obviously mechanical but also oh-so oddly persuasive, as though in some alternative universe she might really be alive.

I have long been fascinated by images of artificial women who seem real. As a child, I was fixated by Rod Serling's television series *The Twilight Zone*—particularly the episode "The After Hours" where a pretty department store customer accidentally finds herself in the store after it has closed for the night and discovers that the mannequins on the ninth floor have strangely come alive and that she herself is really a mannequin.

Images of lifelike mannequins continued to fascinate me in the years ahead. On a trip to Paris I peered through a shop window at a group of stark white unclothed mannequins whose bodies seemed frozen in time yet also animated—like the casts of volcano victims killed at Pompeii in ancient times. At a New York city flea market, I discovered the face of a female mannequin that looked like 1930s film star Marlene Dietrich, and another mannequin's face peering out of a paper bag. When I photographed these mannequins I wanted to capture the blurred line between the artificial and the real (Figs. 9 and 10).

As a scholar, I also wrote about how nineteenth-century artists pictured people who looked like mechanized human beings. My book *Breaking Frame: Technology and the Visual Arts in the Nineteenth Century* (1992) presented artists' satirical views of men and women in the age of steam, including a man walking with steam-powered legs. In my next book, *Women and the Machine: Representations From the Spinning Wheel to the Electronic Age* (2001), I wrote about images of artificial women whose bodies were fashioned through electricity, and real women wearing mechanized fashions: wired crinolines and bustle undergarments that made them move so stiffly and awkwardly that they looked like mechanical dolls.

The idea of artificial women who seemed alive also seemed like an exciting subject for a museum exhibit, and with the enthusiastic help and encouragement of Marcia Rudy, then a vice-president at the New York Hall of Science, I wrote and curated the exhibit "Alluring Androids, Robot Women, and Electronic Eves" which was first exhibited at the museum from June to September 2006.

I would like to give Marcia Rudy and members of the museum's staff many thanks for helping me produce this exhibit. I would also like to thank Dr. Joseph C. Hoffman, Provost and Vice President for Academic Affairs at SUNY Maritime College, for his support and also the Provost's FSA Academic Enrichment Fund for making this Fort Schuyler Press book possible.

I would also like to thank my husband, Averill (Bill) Williams for all of his help, patience, and support. When he retired as Associate General Counsel and a vice president at Amerada Hess Corporation, I'm sure he had no idea that he'd be spending some of his free time helping me proofread a book and work on an exhibit. I thank him for his always-useful feedback and his (mostly) good humor through it all.

Finally, as always, I would like to thank my parents, Goldie and Joseph Wosk, for their steadfast and enduring love and encouragement through all these years. When I was a child, they sent me for art lessons in an artist's studio in my hometown of Chicago where my first assignment was to sketch plaster casts of statues. Who knows, maybe my interest in Pygmalion and his wondrous female statue who comes alive started in that studio so long ago.

ALLURING ANDROIDS, ROBOT WOMEN, AND ELECTRONIC EVES*

JULIE WOSK

T he idea of artificial women who seem alive has fascinated film makers, artists, photographers, video game designers, and robotics engineers. In a pivotal moment during the 2004 Hollywood version of *The Stepford Wives*, the president of the Stepford Men's Society, Mike Wellington, enthusiastically shows newcomer Walter Kresby a short film about the mechanism for transforming their high-power career-women wives into sexy and adoring homemakers who love to cook and clean. Through the wonders of technology, women who might include a CEO or judge are placed into a pink "Female Improvement System Machine" and turned into beautiful androids as obliging and compliant as the push-button appliances they adore.

The new Stepford Wives are perfected copies of the originals and are easily manipulated through remote control. They are so in love with their new appliances that they even mimic the movements of washing machines: at the Simply Stepford Day Spa aerobics class, they imitate a rinse cycle as they whirl around in their perky floral sun dresses chanting "Whoosh, Whoosh!" (Fig. 1).

What makes the film particularly intriguing is that it embodies a recurring theme in film, literature, and art—the idea of creating an artificial female who is the answer to men's dreams. *The Stepford Wives* (based on Ira Levin's 1972 novel) is a spoof that satirizes some of men's enduring ideas about The Perfect Woman: a beautiful female who is a compliant sex slave and domestic servant as well.

The doll-like android wives of Stepford, Connecticut are modern-day versions of artificial women that have been around for thousands of years. The ancient Egyptians, Greeks, and Romans as well as other early cultures created toy female dolls with articulated arms and legs. For children, these dolls would most probably be playthings to imagine stories about, to cherish, and to control (Fig. 2).

Artificial women have also appeared as obliging servants, like the beautiful maidservants made of gold in Homer's epic poem, *The Iliad*, who aided the blacksmith god Hephaestus at his work. In 1624, Italian printmaker Giovanni Battista Braccelli in his series of fanciful etchings *Bizzarie di Varie Figure* created an early image of a machine-woman in her familiar domestic role, her body made of everyday household items including a washboard and broom (Fig. 3). The central theme of a fabricated woman who comes alive has its roots in the ancient Greek myth of Pygmalion. In Ovid's telling of the story, the sculptor Pygmalion of Cyprus creates an ivory sculpture of a beautiful woman and falls in love with his own work of art. He prays to Venus asking the goddess to make the sculpture come alive, and Venus grants his wish, as evocatively portrayed in French artist Jean-Léon Gérôme's painting *Pygmalion and Galatea* (ca. 1890). Here, the beautiful sculpture Galatea is transformed into a flesh-and-blood woman as Pygmalion rapturously holds her in his embrace (Fig. 4).

In Ovid's tale, the sculpture that becomes a real woman is the answer to Pygmalion's deepest wishes and longings, but in later versions, the fabricated lady who comes alive may cause anguish and torment as well. Whether the artificial woman evokes love or fear, fantasies or nightmares, often depends on whether her artificial nature is apparent or artfully concealed. Does she look segmented or seamless, synthetic or real? Does she suddenly—and horrifyingly—turn out to be no more than an artificial, alien creature?

In eighteenth-century Switzerland, two skilled clockmakers created the aura of reality by camouflaging the mechanics of their automatons. When they created their mechanical female musician (Figs. 5 and 6), Pierre and Henri-Louis Jaquet-Droz hid the machinery in furniture and beneath her elegant clothes. Her hidden mechanisms allowed her chest to rise and fall as though she were breathing and her fingers to play Henri-Louis' own musical compositions on an organ in the shape of a harpsichord. To many eighteenth-century observers, the lady musician with her compelling smile seemed astonishingly real (though her somewhat artificial and jerky movements remained a reminder she was only a mechanical creature).

But in later versions of mechanical women, the artifice was at times laid bare. Deconstructing the illusion of reality, the cover illustration of a *Galaxy Science Fiction* magazine from the 1950s depicts a male technician matter-of-factly repairing a blonde-haired female robot, a cutaway view exposing her wired arm and chest (Fig. 7). Her breast and other fragmented body parts lie unceremoniously on the table, a stark reminder that the woman is simply a product of technology and anything but real.

3

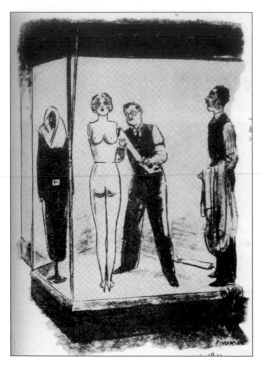

She can be taken apart and reassembled, made ready for practical use in this scientifically-detached world.

(Sometimes, though, the reassembly didn't work that well. In a 1930s American cartoon, two men work in a department store window putting together a female mannequin as one man makes a fundamental error: he connects her upper torso which is facing front to her lower torso which is facing backwards. The other man exclaims, "Good God, Bagby! Don't you know ANYTHING about women?").

DOLLS, MANNEQUINS, AND THE AMBIGUITIES OF THE UNCANNY

The discovery that a beloved woman is nothing more than an artificial segmented creature—an armature for a real human being—can turn out to be a nightmare experience, evoking the type of situation described by Sigmund Freud in his essay on "The Uncanny." Freud described the "uncanny" as a situation creating feelings of uncertainty about "whether a particular figure is a human being or an automaton," and also a situation when "an apparently inanimate being was really alive"—as in German writer E. T. A. Hoffmann's nineteenth-century story, "The Sandman," when the young man Nathanael falls passionately in love with beautiful and perfectly-proportioned Olympia, but is horrified when she turns out to be nothing more than a mechanical doll. Hoffmann's story later inspired Léo Delibes' ballet *Coppélia* and Jacques Offenbach's opera *The Tales of Hoffmann* (in the opera, it is the poet Hoffmann who falls in love with Olympia). In the 1951 film version of the opera, directed by Michael Powell and Emeric Pressburger, Olympia is torn apart by the two feuding men, Coppelius and Spalanzani, and blinks her eyes as Hoffmann looks on, staring in horror at her decapitated head (Fig. 8).

Photographers' images of mannequins and dolls can also embody the idea of the uncanny. Julie Wosk's photographs of mannequins often blur the boundaries between the artificial and the real. These simulated women are inanimate yet eerily alive. The mannequin in *Marlene* (1995, Fig. 10) conjures up the face of film siren Marlene Dietrich, her seductive gaze enticing us into her mysterious world.

Images like *Marlene* suggest some of the paradoxes of being female and the complex nature of women's culturally-constructed identities. Women are often expected to be both artificial and authentic—to wear make-up and look like mannequins yet be genuine as well. They smile at us behind masks of glamor and beauty, masks that may camouflage their secret selves. In Wosk's photograph *Bag Lady* (1992, Fig. 9) photographed in a Manhattan flea market, a mannequin's smiling, half-hidden face peers out of a paper bag. She is artful yet provocatively real—a teasing and packaged social commodity, ready to be transported away.

SIMULATED WOMEN AND THE WORLD OF SCIENCE AND TECHNOLOGY

Images of artificial females not only reveal cultural attitudes about women but also offer a tantalizing insight into how social attitudes toward science and technology have often dramatically changed. In eighteenth and nineteenth-century Europe and America, as well as in countries like China, female automatons were considered ingenious mechanical marvels and were widely admired as examples of their makers' technical expertise.

In the French novel *L'Ève future* (*Tomorrow's Eve*, 1885) by Villiers de l'Isle-Adam, a fictional Thomas Edison uses electricity to create another technological wonder: the beautiful Hadaly who is the exact double of the less-than-perfect Alicia Cary, a singer and the lover of Lord Ewald. For Lord Ewald, the beautiful Hadaly is just what he needs—an identical reproduction of his mistress with none of Alicia's mediocrity of mind.

At the end of the nineteenth century, the real Thomas Edison manufactured his own version of technological females— phonographic dolls mass-produced at Edison's West Orange, New Jersey factory in 1889–90 (Fig. 11). These mechanical dolls were dressed in fashionable clothes and embedded with tiny phonographs that played wax cylinders, reproducing the sound of girls' voices reciting nursery rhymes like "Mary Had a Little Lamb."[1]

But artificial females created through science and technology have also reflected much more pessimistic, dystopian views showing the underside of technology. In the hands of mad scientists and inventors like Rotwang in Fritz Lang's silent film masterpiece *Metropolis* (1927), technology could help create seductive but dangerous females. These women, like the syn-thetic false Maria in *Metropolis*, embodied some of men's deepest longings and fears—longings for an exotic and beautiful female and fears of being endangered by her as well (Figs. 12–16).

In Lang's film, Maria appears as two familiar female archetypes: woman as a saintly, comforting angel and woman as a beautiful, diabolical *femme fatale*, an alluring temptress who leads men astray. Rotwang first creates a metallic female robot and then uses electricity to create an evil android double of the saintly Maria—a sensuous siren who dances seductively before men at a party who look at her with leering eyes. A dangerous double, the demonic false Maria incites the citizens of the metropolis to riot but is later stopped and burned at the stake.[2]

In James Whale's 1935 film, *Bride of Frankenstein*, the artificial woman meant to bring love and fulfillment causes anguish and misery instead. Film star Elsa Lanchester played the role of

Elsa Lanchester as the Bride of Frankenstein

the "bride" fabricated by Dr. Frankenstein to provide a companion for the lonely and tormented Monster, an answer to the Monster's dreams. Produced from a beautiful corpse that has been subjected to electricity, she has streaks of white lightning in her impressively-coifed hair. After emerging from her bandages, however, she takes one look at the Monster and lets out a scream—dashing his hopes forever as she flees from the scene (Fig. 17).

AN OBJECT OF WONDER

The idea of lifelike female robots and androids also intrigued American television writers and producers during the 1960s–1980s. In the 1980s, the television comedy series *Small Wonder* presented a lifelike 10-year old girl robot named Vicki who is brought home to join the family of her inventor, electronics expert Ted Lawson. Lawson works at United Robotronics, and Vicki is the product of the latest technology. As the show's theme song proclaimed, "She's fantastic, made of plastic, microchips here and there; she's a small wonder and brings love and laughter everywhere." In the series, Lawson's young son quickly finds ways to use Vicki to do his bidding—seeing her as a handy housemate to help him clean up his room and put away his clothes. (Fig. 18).

Today, we have again returned to the idea of an android or robot female as an object of wonder, the product of electronic technologies and the creative ingenuity of artists and robotics engineers. Lifelike female androids and avatars in film, animation, and video games draw on the talents of digital artists and a wide range of computer graphics and interactive media professionals. Through the science of electronics, these virtual women seem ever-more alive.

In Hoffmann's story "The Sandman," Nathanael is horrified when Olympia turns out to be nothing more than an automaton or mechanical doll. But the artificial females created by some of today's women multimedia artists can be friendly creatures rather than fearsome beings. Instead of becoming the object of men's gaze, Lynn Hershman Leeson's *Tillie the Telerobotic Doll* (1995–1998) allows us to see the world through the doll's own eyes (Fig. 19).

Some leading female characters in video games have reconfigured the old stereotypes about women themselves. The athletic, adventurous anthropologist Lara Croft in the many versions of the Tomb Raider games still wears skimpy and skin-tight clothes, but challenges conventional images of the witless sexy female who simply serves as a love interest in many popular games (Fig. 20). In the Japanese television animated cartoon series, *Steel Angel Kurumi*, the android heroine is a combination of the old and the new. She is seductive and wears maid's clothes, but is also bred for the military—a female figure both powerful and strong (Fig. 21).

Many of these video game heroines have realistic-looking facial expressions and emotions, and seem to respond as real human beings. Software training kits such as "Female Android Modeling in Maya" by Digital-Tutors using Maya imaging software are a reminder that these women are actually artificial constructions, not real. The kit gives digital artists training in modeling techniques and ways to construct androids step-by-step, part by part—systematically fabricating facsimile females by creating the feet, ankle joints, legs, knees, forearms, upper arms, hands, fingers, wrists, breasts (Fig. 22).

Today's software designers are continuing to work at creating digital females that look and act like actual human beings. Software companies such as Softimage in Canada have produced sophisticated animation software like "Robot Face" to help achieve realistic, lifelike nuances in facial expressions for use in high-end animation, and have helped to make game-playing and animation ever-more exciting (Figs. 23, 24). Digital artists help endow these figures with human emotions by replicating frowns, flaring nostrils, even bulging neck muscles. Some of the world's most lifelike female robots have been created in Japanese robotics labs, like the robot Repliee Q2 co-created by Professor Hiroshi Ishiguro at the Intelligent Robotics Laboratory at Osaka University in Osaka, Japan. The female robot Repliee Q1 (2005) and Repliee Q2, introduced in 2006, represent, to many people, admirable technological ingenuity, revealing the impressive human ability to create lifelike imitations of human figures (Fig. 24). Partially covered with skin-like silicone rather than hard plastic, female androids like Repliee Q2 look uncannily real as robotics engineers continue to work at giving these robots natural-looking facial expressions, speech, and the ability to interact with people in an (almost) human way.[3]

For some skeptics, though, the very idea of a super-lifelike female robot remains a disturbing one, and these robots may generate anxiety when we realize that the naturalistic females are not really alive. Very realistic-looking robots, in their own way, may create what German playwright Bertolt Brecht (referring to drama) called the alienation effect—the alienating or disorienting impact created when the familiar suddenly looks strange.

In his 1982 film *Blade Runner*, director Ridley Scott presents a haunting view of an android's own anguished recognition that she isn't real. The dark-haired beauty Rachael makes the painful and poignant discovery that she is a replicant—a female android with electronically-implanted memories and emotions that feel all-too-real. Deckard, who is assigned to hunt and destroy replicants, himself cannot tell at first if Rachael is actually human.[4]

Like Rachael, today's ultra-realistic female robots also evoke ambiguities and uncertainty about whether they are artificial or not. They raise a troubling question: will these technological wonders prove useful and enhance our lives, or will they profoundly confuse and undermine our own sense of human identity?

WHAT'S AHEAD?

Today's versions of female robots and androids also raise some other provocative questions. In the coming years of the twenty-first century, artists and engineers, film makers and software designers will undoubtedly present us with new forms of artificial females, and new versions of electronic Eves. Will these Eves reinforce old stereotypes or will they reflect actual changes in women themselves? Will new versions of artificial females still embody men's age-old image of perfection: the beautiful, obedient, sexy woman who loves to cook and clean? Will new female robots simply become the very latest in sex toys? As more and more women enter the fields of robotics and game design, will they dramatically change the way artificial women are portrayed? Will the new female replicants of the future world seem alluring, alarming, delightful, scary? We must wait and see.

NOTES

1. At the time, these young women in Edison's factories were thought by some to resemble automatons or mechanical creatures themselves because of the way they kept repeating the rhymes. See Julie Wosk, *Breaking Frame: Technology and the Visual Arts in the Nineteenth Century* (New Brunswick, N. J.: Rutgers University Press, 1992), pp. 84–85, and the book's Chapter Two on mechanized human beings.

2. For more on *Metropolis*, female automatons, and other artificial women, see Julie Wosk, *Women and the Machine: Representations from the Spinning Wheel to the Electronic Age* (Baltimore: Johns Hopkins University Press, 2001, paperbound 2003).

3. Also in 2006, Professor Ishiguro in collaboration with the Japanese Kokoro Company created the Actroid DER and Actroid DER2 robots that the company called "Elegant, feminine, and lively at all times." These

robots were available for rental and came in varied costumes, including one dressed as an information booth attendant and another in a "cute maid costume at [a] trendy coffee shop."

4. The film was based on Philip K. Dick's novel *Do Androids Dream of Electric Sheep?* Ironically, it is uncertain whether Deckard himself is real or a replicant. In another version of an unnerving discovery, the episode titled "The After Hours" (1960) in Rod Serling's famed television series *The Twilight Zone* presents a department store customer Marsha White who gets locked in the store at night. She is soon startled to discover that her female store clerk is really a mannequin and she herself is one too—a mannequin who has been allowed to spend a month outside among "normal" people. At the episode's end, she must go back to simply being a "wooden lady with a painted face."

ILLUSTRATIONS

Fig. 1. The Stepford Wives at the Simply Stepford Day Spa, from the 2004 satiric Hollywood film *The Stepford Wives*, based on Ira Levin's 1972 novel of the same name. Photo reproduced courtesy of Paramount Licensing.

In the 2004 Hollywood film version of *The Stepford Wives* (a remake of the 1975 film), women of Stepford, Connecticut who were formerly high-achieving professionals have been transformed by a machine into glamorous, compliant wives. The remote-controlled android-wives are in love with their roles as homemakers and always want to look their best. Even at their Simply Stepford Day Spa aerobics classes they wear sexy sundresses and high heels.

All captions © 2008 Julie Wosk

Fig. 2. Ancient Greek dolls. Illustration from Max
Von Boehn, *Dolls and Puppets*, 1932.

Ancient Greek dolls were often made of clay or wood. The dolls were most often female figures and frequently had moveable arms and legs.

Fig. 3. Etching of Woman Made of Household Tools by Giovanni Battista Braccelli, *Bizzarie di Varie Figure*, 1624. Photo reproduced courtesy of the Octavo Corporation.

Braccelli was an artist and engraver from Florence who created a suite of fanciful figures, including this machine-woman composed of a washboard, spoon, and other domestic wares.

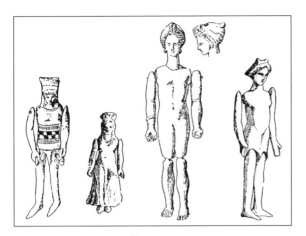

Figure 2

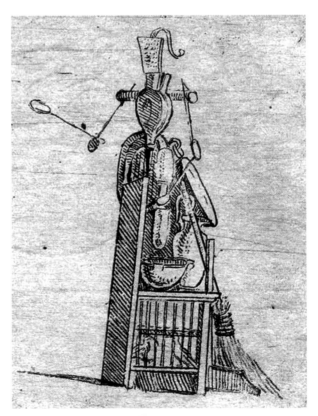

Figure 3

Fig. 4. Poster, Metropolitan Museum of Art, New York, of Jean-Léon Gérôme's oil painting *Pygmalion and Galatea* (ca. 1890).

The image of the beautiful simulated woman who comes alive is a recurring theme in men's fantasies. In Ovid's classic tale, Pygmalion was King of Cyprus and a sculptor who fell in love with his own artistic creation, a beautiful woman made of ivory. During the festival of Venus, he prayed to the goddess asking her for a wife "like the ivory maid." Venus grants him his wish, and brings his beautiful sculpture to life. Pygmalion married the now-human woman, who later writers named Galatea.

Fig. 5. Lady Musician, an automaton created by Pierre and Henri-Louis Jaquet-Droz in 1783, Musée d' art et d'histoire, Neuchâtel, Switzerland.

This female automaton created by master Swiss watch and clockmakers Pierre and his son Henri-Louis Jaquet Droz was highly admired in an age infatuated with mechanical wonders. Eighteenth-century Europeans made pilgrimages to see her in Neuchâtel, Switzerland, and she was exhibited in the major capitals and courts of Europe, including Paris, London, Madrid, and Kazan in Russia.

The automaton is about 4 feet high, and plays five melodies on a type of organ designed in the shape of an early harpsichord or clavicin. The music was composed by Henri-Louis Jaquet-Droz himself. The automaton's interior mechanisms feature levers that enable her to move her eyes from side to side as she plays and her chest rises and falls as though she were breathing. While playing she also turns her head around, looks left and right, casts her eyes down and looks up, bends forward and straightens, and takes a bow at the end of each melody.

Fig. 6. Detail of the mechanism of the Lady Musician's hand.

Unlike other mechanical automatons that simply look like they are playing, the fingers of the Jaquet-Droz Lady Musician actually do the playing.
Her fingers are driven by two cylinders with pegs (similar to the cylinders in a music box) contained in her torso. The pegs move a complex
set of levers that are connected through her arms to her fingers, causing
them to press the keys on the organ which produces musical notes.

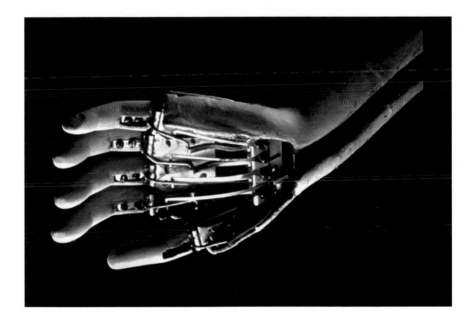

Fig. 7. Scientist Making Repairs on Robot Woman. Illustration by EMSH (Edmund Alexander Emshwiller), *Galaxy Science Fiction* magazine, September 1954.

Ed Emshwiller was an abstract expressionist painter who produced cover and interior illustrations for science fiction magazines from 1951-79, and also made experimental films and videos. In this magazine cover illustration, exposed wires and fragmented sections of the woman's breast lying on the table are a startling reminder that she is actually a mechanical apparatus rather than real.

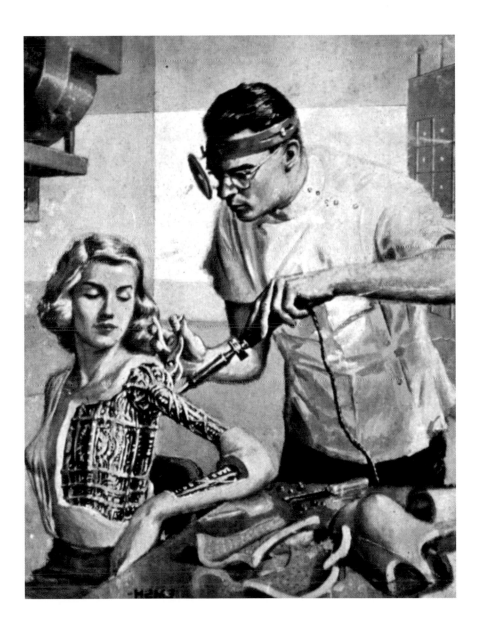

Fig. 8. *The Tales of Hoffmann* (British film, 1951) with Moira Shearer as Olympia and Robert Rounseville as Hoffmann. Photo courtesy of Photofest.

Female automatons could be associated with the macabre. In the story "The Sandman" (1817) by German writer E. T. A. Hoffmann, Nathanael falls passionately in love with the beautiful Olympia who is actually a mechanical young woman created by Coppelius and Spalanzani. He dances with her and is enchanted by her but later watches in horror as the two men fight over her, twisting her body until her eyes fall out on the ground. Gazing at her limp body and waxen face, the now-wretched Nathanael at last recognizes she isn't real.

In the 1951 film version of Offenbach's opera *The Tales of Hoffmann*, directed by Michael Powell and Emeric Pressburger, it is the poet Hoffmann who falls in love with Olympia and looks on in horror as the two men tear her apart, leaving him to gaze in shock at her severed head.

BL19-82A

Fig. 9. Julie Wosk, *Bag Lady*, 1992. C-Print. © Julie Wosk.

Photographed in a Manhattan flea market, this blue-eyed mannequin captures us with her teasing smile though her identity is half concealed.

Fig. 10. Julie Wosk, *Marlene*, 1995. C-Print © Julie Wosk.

The simulated women in Julie Wosk's photographs are artful and alluring, synthetic yet provocatively real. In *Marlene*, a mannequin resembling 1930s film star Marlene Dietrich eyes us seductively from beneath her velvet hat as she lures us into her simulated world.

Fig. 11. Phonographic doll manufactured by Thomas Edison at his West Orange, New Jersey plant, 1889–90.

Edison's phonographic dolls had German-made bisque heads, jointed wooden limbs, and a steel torso that housed a miniature motorized phonograph with a wax cylinder and a small needle that traced the grooves in the cylinder. The talking mechanism was located inside the doll's chest and wound by hand. To create the sounds, young girls working at Edison's New Jersey plant sat in a room and recorded words to nursery rhymes and other songs onto the cylinders. A few years later the French doll manufacturer Jumeau produced its own phonographic dolls which had cylinders that allowed the dolls to sing in French, English, or Spanish.

Fig. 12. The scientist Rotwang with the metallic female robot he created in Fritz Lang's classic silent film *Metropolis*, 1927.

In Fritz Lang's silent movie masterpiece, Maria appears as two familiar female archetypes: woman as saintly, comforting angel and woman as diabolical temptress who leads men astray. The angelic Maria offers comfort to oppressed workers of the city, but this worries the Master of the Metropolis, Fredersen, who asks the mad scientist Rotwang to build a robot in Maria's likeness to sow discord among the workers and destroy their confidence in her.

The android version of Maria is created through electricity amidst flashing rays and floating rings of light. Rotwang , who had earlier created a stylized metallic female robot, connects the robot through cables to the real Maria encased in a glass box. Subjected to electricity, the robot is transformed into Maria's exact double. The "evil" android Maria is a seductive dancer who entices the workers and leads them to riot. The real Maria escapes to safety while her diabolical double is burned at the stake, reverting to a robot once again.

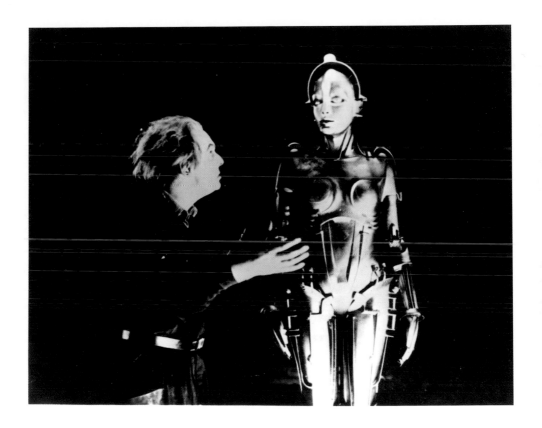

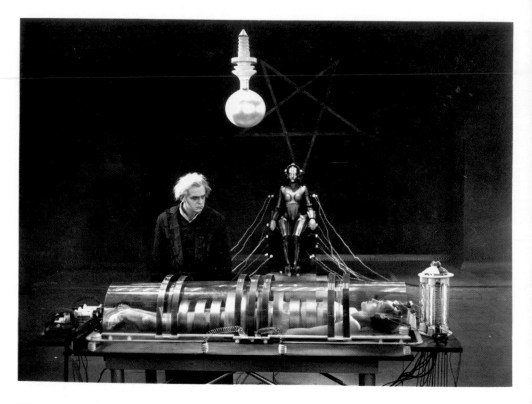

Fig. 13. In *Metropolis,* the saintly Maria lies in a glass tube while her body is used to create a robot copy of her as the scientist Rotwang looks on.

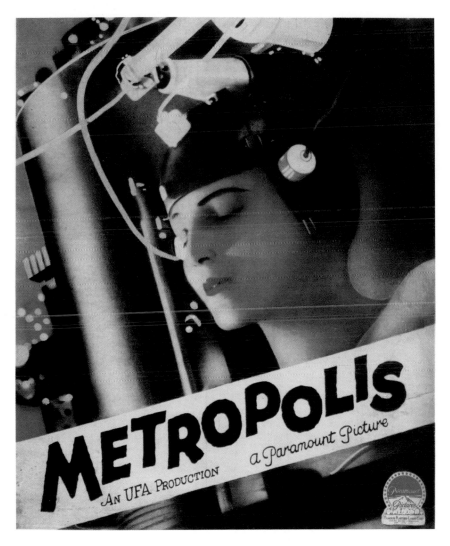

Fig. 14. Poster for the American release of *Metropolis* picturing Maria lying in the glass tube.

Fig. 15. The "good" Maria, played by German actress Brigitte Helm, offering comfort to the children of the Metropolis in Fritz Lang's film.

Fig. 16. The evil android version of Maria, also played by actress Brigitte Helm in the film *Metropolis*, is both seductive and dangerous—a sultry siren who leads men astray.

Fig. 17. The Monster played by actor Boris Karloff and the Monster's Mate played by Elsa Lanchester in James Whale's 1935 film *Bride of Frankenstein*, a sequel to the movie *Frankenstein*, based very loosely on Mary Shelley's novel *Frankenstein*, first published in 1818.

James Whale's film used elaborate special effects to depict the creation of a woman who was designed to offer comfort but produces anguish instead. The film's mad scientist is the maniacal Dr. Pretorius who blackmails Henry Frankenstein into collaborating on a mate for the Monster, (though in Mary Shelley's novel, the Monster's mate is destroyed by Dr. Frankenstein before he actually finishes it). Elsa Lanchester not only played the role of the bride in Whale's film but also the role of Mary Shelley herself.

Fig. 18. Vicki being introduced to the Lawson Family in the 1980s television sitcom *Small Wonder*. Photo courtesy of Photofest.

In this American television sitcom that ran from 1985–89, Tiffany Brissette played the 10-year old robot V.I. C. I. (Voice Input Child Identicant) nicknamed Vicki. With synthetic skin and actual human hair she looks like a real little girl. Some of the giveaways that she's not actually real are that she speaks in a flat, emotionless monotone, repeats programmed phrases, and can rotate her head 180 degrees. Vicki's electronics are stored underneath a flap in her back, and she is controlled by computer and voice commands. She quickly becomes part of the household of her creator, Ted Lawson, and a pal for their young son Jamie. In no time, Vicki proves herself useful by doing Jamie's homework.

Fig. 19. Lynn Hershman Leeson, *Tillie, The Telerobotic Doll*, 1995–98.

Photo courtesy Lynn Hershman Leeson and bitforms gallery, New York.

Today's women artists are reconfiguring the idea of android and doll. Artist Lynn Hershman Leeson created what she calls "synthetic female agents," including *Tillie, the Telerobotic Doll* which was situated in a gallery space and had cameras for "eyes"—a video camera in the left eye and a Webcam in the right. The left eye, which "saw" in color, recorded what was directly in front of the doll in the gallery. The right eye, which could be controlled on the Web by clicking on an "eye con," allowed participants to turn the doll's head 180 degrees and survey the gallery space. Using Tillie's eyes as an extension of their own, participants themselves became, in the artist's words, "virtual cyborgs."

Fig. 20. Lara Croft, the athletic, intelligent, powerful and sexy star of the Tomb Raider video game series.© Eido Interactive.

Video games during the early 1980s through the mid 1990s were primarily designed with male users in mind, with male characters as the heroes and females simply serving as victims or the love interest in the story. Starting in 1996, with the introduction of characters like Lara Croft in the Tomb Raider series, men and women game players found a new kind of female avatar in video games. Lara, an archaeologist whose father is a British lord, goes on global adventures to exotic and remote areas to discover mythic artifacts in legendary cities like Atlantis and in an ancient tomb in Egypt. She uses dual pistols, one in each hand, rides a motorcycle, and loves to explore remote areas in the world. As a virtual woman, Lara counters female stereotypes in video games by being strong, intrepid, and athletic even though she still has a sexy body and wears skimpy clothes.

Fig. 21. Steel Angel Kurumi, a powerful artificial woman with pink hair and dressed in a French maid's outfit in the Japanese anime of the same name. © Kaishaku/Kadokawa Shoten-PONY CANYON Inc., Verbiage Present: Image Provided Courtesy of ADV Films.

In this television anime introduced in 2002 and set in a fanciful Japan of the 1920s, the sexy and powerful Steel Angel named Kurumi created by Dr. Ayanokouji is activated when she accidentally receives a kiss from the adolescent boy Nakahito in the first episode. The two try to evade the military who want to use Karumi for warfare, and her story continues into the twenty-first century *in Steel Angel* 2.

Fig. 22. Illustration by Kyle Green for *Female Android Modeling in Maya*, software by Digital-Tutors/PL Studios Inc., Oklahoma City, Oklahoma.

The software kit *Female Android Modeling in Maya* by Digital-Tutors/ PL Studios gives artists step-by-step instruction in using Maya 3D modeling software to create images of female androids for use in high-end animation and video games.

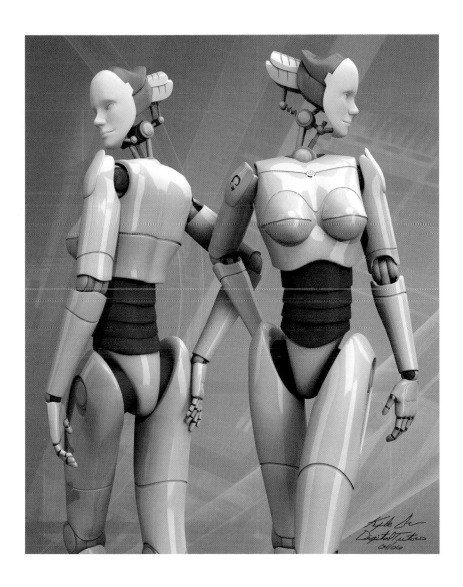

Fig. 23. "Kitty Hunting" from software Softimage Face Robot SOFTIM-AGE (R)/FACE ROBOT (tm) v.1.0 is software introduced by Softimage Co., headquartered in Canada and a subsidiary of Avid Technology, Inc. in Tewksbury (01876).

Designed for 3D face animation, this software uses a computer model of facial soft tissue to mimic the full range of human emotions. It allows artists to give characters facial expressions and makes it easier to image details like wrinkles, frowns, flaring nostrils, and bulging neck muscles. The software is intended for use in high-end animation, post-production, and games.

Fig. 23.

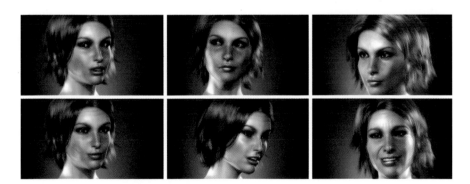

Fig. 24. Detail of the types of facial expressions that can be made using Soft-image Face Robot software.

This software can help endow simulated women with expressions including intrigued, mean, melancholy, thoughtful.

Fig. 25. Repliee Q2, developed by Professor Hiroshi Ishiguro and KOKORO Co. Ltd. Professor Ishiguro is in the Department of Adaptive Machine Systems, Graduate School of Engineering, Osaka University, Osaka, Japan.

The lifelike female robot Repliee Q2 was introduced in February 2006 as an upgraded version of Repliee Q1 (2005), a woman partially covered with skin-like silicone who could gesture, blink her eyes, and seemed to breathe as her chest rose and fell. Powered by a near-by air compressor, the robot had 31 points of articulation in the upper body.

Repliee Q2 was designed to be more lifelike. The robot can make some facial expressions and mouth shapes, and responds to touch. She is covered with skin sensors, and if she is tapped on the shoulder, she even shows some attitude: she turns and says in English, "Hey, what's your problem!"